Contents

Acknowledgements

The publisher wishes to thank the following for their help with the reading and production of the book: Maz Loton, Jon Moore and Cathy Turner. Thanks are also due to Laura Ingham for her designs for this series.

The publisher is indebted to the Association of Accounting Technicians for its kind permission for the reproduction of its sample assessment in this text.

Author and Technical Editor

Aubrey Penning, the author, until recently co-ordinated the AAT courses at Worcester College of Technology, and taught a range of units including Management Accounting and the two taxation Units. He has over twenty years experience of teaching accountancy on a variety of courses in Worcester and Gwent. He is a Certified Accountant, and before his move into full-time teaching he worked for the health service, a housing association and a chemical supplier. Aubrey is author of *Business Taxation*, *Budgeting* and *Financial Performance* and co-author of *Basic Costing* and *Cash Management*, all published by Osborne Books.

Bob Thomas, the Technical Editor of this book, has been involved with the Education and Training activities of the AAT since 1986, including the development and piloting of the skills-based scheme. He is an external verifier, a simulation writer, a moderator and a contributor at workshops, training days, conferences and master classes. Until recently he was a member of the Learning and Development Board and Chairman of the Assessment Panel.

Business taxation 2011/12

Workb

for Finar

Aubrey Penning

Bob Thomas

osborne
BOOKS

Published by Osborne Books Limited
Unit 1B Everoak Estate
Bromyard Road
Worcester WR2 5HP
Tel 01905 748071
Email books@osbornebooks.co.uk
Website www.osbornebooks.co.uk

Design by Laura Ingham
Cover and page design image © Istockphoto.com/Petrovich9

Printed by CPI Antony Rowe Limited, Chippenham

British Library Cataloguing in Publication Data
A catalogue record for this book is available from the British Library

ISBN 978 1905777 716

Introduction

what this book covers

This book has been written specifically to cover Learning Area 'Business Tax' which combines two QCF Units in the AAT Level 4 Diploma in Accounting:

■ Principles of business tax

■ Calculating business tax

This book has been designed to include guidance and exercises based on Tax Year 2011/12 (Finance Act 2011). We understand that the AAT plan to assess this legislation from March 2012 to March 2013. Tutors and students are advised to check this with the AAT and ensure that they sit the correct Computer Based Assessment.

what this book contains

This book is set out in two sections:

■ **Chapter activities** which provide extra practice material in addition to the activities included in the Osborne Books Tutorial text. Answers to the Chapter Activities are set out in this book.

■ **Practice assessments** are included to prepare the student for the Computer Based Assessments. They are based directly on the structure, style and content of the sample assessment material provided by the AAT at www.aat.org.uk. Suggested answers to the Practice Assessments are set out in this book.

online support from Osborne Books

This book is supported by practice material available at www.osbornebooks.co.uk

This material is available to tutors – and to students at their discretion – in two forms:

■ A **Tutor Zone** which is available to tutors who have adopted the Osborne Books texts. This area of the website provides extra assessment practice material (plus answers) in addition to the activities included in this Workbook text.

■ **E-learning** – online practice questions designed to familiarise students with the style of the AAT Computer Based Assessments.

further information

If you want to know more about our products, please visit www.osbornebooks.co.uk, email books@osbornebooks.co.uk or telephone Osborne Books Customer Services on 01905 748071.

Chapter activities

1

Chapter activities

Introduction to business taxation

1.1 Which of the following statements are correct?

✓

	True	False
(a) A self employed taxpayer must pay Class 2 NIC, unless the 'small earnings exception' is claimed		
(b) Class 4 NIC is payable by the self employed only when drawings are over £7,225		
(c) Class 4 NIC is payable by the self employed when profits are over £7,225		
(d) Class 4 NIC is paid throughout the tax year		
(e) Class 4 NIC is payable at 2% for profits over £42,475		

1.2 Using the following table, insert the details and dates relating to online returns and payment of tax

	Period return relates to	Latest return submission date	Latest tax payment date
Corporation Tax			
Income Tax			

Select from the following:

- Tax year
- Financial year
- 12 months after end of tax year
- 12 months after end of chargeable accounting period
- 9 months and one day after end of chargeable accounting period
- 12 months after end of period that accounts are based on
- Chargeable accounting period
- 31 January following tax year
- 31 October following tax year

1.3

   (1)   A taxpayer has self employed income of £60,000 for the tax year 2011/12. The amount chargeable to NIC at 9% would be

       £

   (2)   A taxpayer has self employed income of £45,000 for the tax year 2011/12. The amount of total Class 4 NIC payable would be

       £

1.4   State whether each of the following is true or false.   ✓

	True	False
(a) A self employed individual's tax records relating to his business for 2011/12 need to be kept until 31 January 2018, or longer if an investigation is being carried out.		
(b) HMRC has a right to visit premises to inspect records.		
(c) Accountants must normally follow the rules of confidentiality, but there are exceptions.		
(d) Where a practitioner has knowledge or suspicion that his client is money laundering, then he has a duty to inform the relevant person or authority.		
(e) AAT guidelines on professional ethics apply to AAT members, but not to AAT students.		
(f) When an accountant is advising a client the greatest duty of care is to HMRC.		

1.5   State the final submission dates for tax returns for the following businesses.

A sole trader with accounts made up to 31 March 2012.	
A sole trader with accounts made up to 30 June 2012.	
A limited company with accounts made up to 31 December 2011.	

2

Chapter activities

Corporation tax – trading profits

2.1 A limited company has the income and expenses as shown in the following table recorded in its income statement. In order to calculate the adjusted trading profit, some items need to be added and some deducted from the net profit shown in the income statement. Some items do not require any adjustment.

Analyse the income and expenses, by ticking the appropriate columns in the table.

✓

	Add to net profit	Deduct from net profit	No adjustment required
Depreciation			
Discount received			
Directors' salaries			
Dividends received			
Rent receivable			
Rent payable			
Interest payable			
Advertising costs			
Entertaining customers			

2.2 River Limited has the following summarised income statement.

	£	£
Sales		120,000
less cost of sales		35,000
gross profit		85,000
add gain on sale of non-current asset		12,000
		97,000
less expenses:		
administration expenses	18,000	
depreciation	13,000	
charitable payments (gift-aid)	2,000	
entertaining staff	5,000	
vehicle expenses	22,000	
		60,000
Net profit		37,000

Select the adjusted trading profit (before capital allowances) from the following.

		✓
(a)	£57,000	
(b)	£45,000	
(c)	£40,000	
(d)	£34,000	
(e)	£37,000	
(f)	£38,000	

2.3 State whether the following statements are true or false.   ✓

	True	False
(a) The basis of assessment for trading profits is the tax adjusted trading profits of the chargeable accounting period, prepared on an accruals basis.		
(b) Lease rental payments for cars are never allowable as they are deemed to be capital expenditure.		
(c) Interest payable on trade loans is not allowable.		
(d) If a loan to an employee is written off the amount is not an allowable deduction.		
(e) Donations to political parties are an allowable expense.		
(f) Employers' national insurance contributions are not an allowable deduction as they are effectively a form of taxation.		
(g) Employees' parking fines incurred while on business are an allowable deduction.		

2.4 If an accounting period is longer than 12 months, which of the following statements shows the correct approach?

✓

(a) Provided the accounting period is not more than 18 months long, the whole period can form one chargeable accounting period.	
(b) The capital allowances are calculated for the long accounting period and deducted from the adjusted trading profits for the long accounting period. This is then time-apportioned into two chargeable accounting periods.	
(c) It is illegal to prepare accounts for a limited company for more than 12 months, so the problem does not arise.	
(d) The trading profits for the long accounting period are time-apportioned into two periods before tax adjustments are carried out to each period's profit. Capital allowances are calculated for the long period and then time-apportioned, before being deducted from each period's adjusted profits.	
(e) The trading profits for the long period are adjusted for tax purposes (before capital allowances), and the result is time-apportioned into two chargeable accounting periods. Separate capital allowance computations are carried out for each chargeable accounting period, and then deducted from each of the adjusted trading profits.	

2.5   A limited company has the following tax-adjusted results for years to 31 December 2010 and 2011:

	2010	2011
Trading Income	£50,000	£0
Income from Investments	£18,000	£15,000
Chargeable Gains	£0	£10,000

The company made a trading loss in 2011 of £81,000.

What is the maximum amount of loss that could be set against the taxable total profits for 2010?

	✓
(a) £56,000	
(b) £68,000	
(c) £50,000	
(d) £66,000	
(e) £0	

3

Chapter activities

Corporation tax – capital allowances

3.1 Analyse the following items into those that qualify as plant and machinery for capital allowance purposes, (under corporation tax) and those that do not, by ticking the appropriate column.

✓

	Qualifying	Not qualifying
Car for employee's private use		
Office furniture		
Capital expenditure on software		
Payments for vehicle on operating lease		
Vehicles bought on credit		
Buildings		
Equipment bought through hire purchase		

3.2 A company has a 12-month chargeable accounting period ending on 31/3/2012, with no written down values brought forward for capital allowance purposes. During the period the company purchased:

■ A new low-emission car for £26,000

■ A car with emissions of 180 g/km for £22,000

■ Plant for £60,000

Calculate the maximum capital allowances that can be claimed, and insert the figures into the following sentences.

The AIA that can be claimed is £

The first year allowance that can be claimed at 100% is £

The writing down allowance that can be claimed at 20% is £

The writing down allowance that can be claimed at 10% is £

The total capital allowance that can be claimed is £

3.3 Analyse each of the following capital acquisitions into the relevant category by ticking the appropriate column.

✓

	AIA (to limit)	20% WDA Main Pool	10% WDA Special Rate Pool	100% FYA
Car emissions of 185 g/km				
Car emissions of 99 g/km				
Machinery				
Zero-emission goods vehicle				
Car emissions of 135 g/km				
Water-efficient plant				

3.4 State whether the following statements are true or false.

✓

	True	False
(a) For a CAP of 9 months, the AIA for each acquisition that qualifies would be scaled down to 9/12 of its cost. For example, an asset bought for £20,000 would only be entitled to £15,000 AIA.		
(b) For a CAP of 9 months any writing down allowance would be scaled down to 9/12 of the equivalent amount for a 12 month period, but first year allowances and balancing allowances would not be affected.		
(c) For a CAP of 9 months any first year allowance would be scaled down to 9/12 of the equivalent amount for a 12 month period, but writing down allowances and balancing allowances would not be affected.		
(d) For a CAP of 9 months the annual investment allowance (AIA) limit would be 9/12 of £100,000 = £75,000.		
(e) For a CAP of 9 months the limit of writing down allowance of £3,000 that applies to existing expensive cars is unaffected.		

3.5 A company has the following information regarding its non-current assets for a 12-month CAP, ending on 31/12/2011.

	£
Written down values brought forward:	
General (main) pool	120,000
Finance Director's car (50% business use) Saab	19,000
Sales Director's car (100% business use) BMW	16,000
Additions:	
Machinery	105,500
New car for Sales Director (emissions 190 g/km)	35,000
Disposals:	
Machinery	5,000
Sales Director's car (BMW)	7,000

Calculate the maximum capital allowances for the CAP.

4 Chapter activities

Corporation tax – chargeable gains

4.1 Select the appropriate disposal proceeds amount to be used in the chargeable gains computation of a limited company by ticking the appropriate column.

✓

	Actual Proceeds	Market Value	£6,000	Zero
Sale of asset for £15,000 to Director who owns 80% of shares in company. Market value of asset is £35,000.				
Gift of asset to unconnected individual (non-shareholder).				
Sale of asset to company employee (non-shareholder) at below market value.				
Sale of chattel for £4,000 (its market value) that had originally cost £10,000.				
Destruction of an uninsured asset during fire.				
Sale of asset for £15,000 to Director who owns 10% of shares in company. Market value of asset is £35,000.				
Shares owned in an unconnected company that have become worthless due to the company's liquidation.				

4.2 Tousist Ltd sold an antique office desk for £10,000 in June 2011. This was bought for £3,500 in August 2000. The indexation factor from August 2000 to June 2011 was 0.379.

Complete the following computation:

Proceeds £ _____

Cost £ _____

Indexation allowance £ _____

Gain £ _____

Chattel restriction on gain £ _____

State whether the chattel restriction will have any effect on the original gain. yes / no

4.3   Penfold Ltd bought 8,000 shares in Tempter Ltd for £19,500 in October 2001. A rights issue of 1 for 40 shares was bought in July 2003 for £1.80 per share. In June 2011, Penfold Ltd sold 6,000 of the shares for £4 per share.

Indexation factors were: October 2001 to July 2003: 0.114; July 2003 to June 2011: 0.297

What is the gain made on the share disposal?

	No. Shares	Cost £	Indexed Cost £

Proceeds	£
Indexed Cost	£
Gain	£

4.4   Treacle Ltd sold a 2 acre plot of land for £40,000 in June 2011. This was part of a 6 acre plot that was bought for £90,000 in August 2000. The 4 acres that were retained were valued at £60,000 in June 2011. The indexation factor from August 2000 to June 2011 was 0.379.

Complete the following computation:

Proceeds   £ _____

Cost   £ _____

Indexation allowance
(before restriction)   £ _____

Gain or (Loss)   £ _____

4.5   Trapper Ltd sold a painting for £5,500 in June 2011. This was bought for £7,500 in August 2000. The indexation factor from August 2000 to June 2011 was 0.379.

Complete the following computation:

Proceeds   £ _____

Cost   £ _____

Indexation allowance   £ _____

Gain or (Loss)   £ _____

5 Chapter activities
Corporation tax – calculating the tax

5.1 Exe Limited is a trading company with no associated companies. For the year ended 31/3/2012 it had the following tax adjusted results:

	£
Trading Profits	600,000
Rental Income	100,000
Dividends Received	45,000

Calculate the corporation tax, using the following table.

	£
Corporation Tax at Main Rate	
Marginal Relief	
Corporation Tax Payable	

5.2 Wye Ltd is a trading company with one associated company. It has the following results for the 8 month CAP to 31/12/2011.

	£
Trading Profits	330,000
Chargeable Gains	40,000
Gift Aid Payments	10,000

Calculate the corporation tax, using the following table.

	£
Maximum of Band	
Corporation Tax at Main Rate	
Marginal Relief	
Corporation Tax Payable	

5.3 Different types of losses can be relieved in different ways. From the list below, select one rule that can apply to each of the losses stated in the table.

Loss	Rules that can apply
Trading Loss	
Capital Loss	
Rental Loss	

Select from:

(a) Set against current period taxable total profits (TTP), with any unused amount carried forward and set against future taxable total profits (TTP)

(b) Set against chargeable gains of same CAP, with any unused loss set against taxable total profits (TTP) of current period

(c) Set against chargeable gains of same CAP, with any unused loss set against chargeable gains of previous period

(d) Set against current period taxable total profits (TTP), with any unused amount carried forward and set against future chargeable gains

(e) Set against trading profits of following CAP

(f) Set against chargeable gains of same CAP, with any unused loss set against chargeable gains of following period

5.4   Xenopus Limited has the following results for the year ended 31/3/2012:

Trading Profits	£1,350,000
Rental Income	£ 250,000
Chargeable Gains	£ 220,000
Dividends Received	£ 180,000

The company also has the following losses brought forward from the previous CAP:

Trade Losses	£ 130,000
Capital Losses	£ 50,000

Xenopus Limited does not have any associated companies.

Complete page 2 of the short CT600 Corporation Tax Return for Xenopus Limited, including the tax calculation.

A blank form is shown opposite.

Page 2

Company tax calculation

Turnover

1   Total turnover from trade or profession   **1** £

Income

3   Trading and professional profits   **3** £

4   Trading losses brought forward claimed against profits   **4** £

box 3 minus box 4

5   Net trading and professional profits   **5** £

6   Bank, building society or other interest, and profits and gains from non-trading loan relationships   **6** £

11   Income from UK land and buildings   **11** £

14   Annual profits and gains not falling under any other heading   **14** £

Chargeable gains

16   Gross chargeable gains   **16** £

17   Allowable losses including losses brought forward   **17** £

box 16 minus box 17

18   Net chargeable gains   **18** £

sum of boxes 5, 6, 11, 14 & 18

21   Profits before other deductions and reliefs   **21** £

Deductions and Reliefs

24   Management expenses under S75 ICTA 1988   **24** £

30   Trading losses of this or a later accounting period under S393A ICTA 1988   **30** £

31   *Put an 'X' in box 31 if amounts carried back from later accounting periods are included in box 30*   **31**

32   Non-trade capital allowances   **32** £

35   Charges paid   **35** £

box 21 minus boxes 24, 30, 32 and 35

37   Profits chargeable to corporation tax   **37** £

Tax calculation

38   Franked investment income   **38** £

39   Number of associated companies in this period   **39**
or

40   Associated companies in the first financial year   **40**

41   Associated companies in the second financial year   **41**

42   *Put an 'X' in box 42 if the company claims to be charged at the starting rate or the small companies' rate on any part of its profits, or is claiming marginal rate relief*   **42**

Enter how much profit has to be charged and at what rate of tax

Financial year *(yyyy)*	Amount of profit	Rate of tax	Tax	
43	**44** £	**45**	**46** £	p
53	**54** £	**55**	**56** £	p

total of boxes 46 and 56

63   Corporation tax   **63** £   p

64   Marginal rate relief   **64** £   p

65   Corporation tax net of marginal rate relief   **65** £   p

66   Underlying rate of corporation tax   **66**   •   %

67   Profits matched with non-corporate distributions   **67**

68   Tax at non-corporate distributions rate   **68** £   p

69   Tax at underlying rate on remaining profits   **69** £   p

See note for box 70 in CT600 Guide

70   **Corporation tax chargeable**   **70** £   p

CT600 (Short) (2008) Version 2

5.5 State whether the following statements are true or false. ✓

		True	False
(a)	Companies must inform HMRC within 6 months that they have started trading. The penalty for failing to notify is £3,000.		
(b)	The flat penalty for failure to submit a Corporation Tax Return on time is £100 for up to 3 months late and £200 for over three months late. A percentage penalty based on the Corporation Tax can also apply.		
(c)	Interest is charged on late payments (including instalments). The interest charged is an allowable deduction against non-trading interest.		
(d)	Errors in tax returns caused by a lack of reasonable care can suffer a penalty of between 0% and 50% of the extra tax due.		
(e)	Failure to keep records can result in a penalty of £3,000 per chargeable accounting period.		
(f)	Errors in tax returns that are both deliberate and concealed are subject to a penalty of up to 100% of the extra tax due.		
(g)	Records need to be kept for at least 6 years from the end of the accounting period.		

6 Chapter activities
Income tax – trading profits

6.1 From the following factors, tick those that are considered the 'badges of trade' which are used to determine whether an individual is trading.

✓

	Badges of Trade
Reason for acquisition and sale of item(s)	
Whether individual enjoys carrying out the activity	
Whether there is a profit motive	
How long the individual has owned the item(s) before sale	
Whether the individual only sells via computer sites	
Whether any supplementary work is carried out on the item(s) before sale	
Whether the individual considers the activity to be his hobby	
How often the individual carries out similar transactions	
Whether the items bought and sold (the subject matter) are used personally by the individual before sale	

6.2 Analyse the following expenditure of a sole trader into those that are allowable deductions for tax purposes and those that are not, by ticking the appropriate column.

✓

	Allowable expenditure	Non-allowable expenditure
Cost of sales		
Entertaining staff		
Fines for lawbreaking by business owner		
Gifts of food or drink to customers		
Trade bad debts written off		
Salary and NIC of business owner		
Depreciation		
Loss on sale of non-current assets		

6.3   Laura Little is a sole trader. Her business has the following income statement:

	£	£
Turnover		1,256,000
Cost of sales		815,400
Gross profit		440,600
Wages and salaries	120,560	
Rent, rates and insurance	51,210	
Repairs to plant	8,615	
Advertising and entertaining	19,535	
Accountancy and legal costs	5,860	
Motor expenses	50,030	
Telephone and office costs	18,050	
Depreciation	22,020	
Other expenses	32,410	328,290
Net Profit		112,310

Notes:

1.   Laura took goods from the business that cost £1,200 and would normally sell for £2,000. The cost is included in cost of sales.

2.   Wages and salaries include: £

Laura Little   45,000

Laura's son, who works during the school holidays   28,000

3.   Advertising and entertaining includes: £

Gifts to customers:

Bottles of wine costing £12 each   2,400

400 mouse mats carrying the business's logo   600

4.   Motor expenses include: £

Delivery van expenses   10,150

Laura's car expenses (used for business only)   5,900

Laura's son's car expenses (used only for private use)   3,800

5.   Other expenses include: £

Cost of staff training   3,150

Increase in general bad debt provision   2,600

6.   Capital allowances have already been calculated at £10,400

Complete the adjusted trading profits computation.

6.4 Mavis Deacon has a 12-month accounting period, with no written down values brought forward for capital allowance purposes. During the period she purchased:

■ A van with 20% private use for £18,000

■ A car with emissions of 130 g/km and 40% private use for £20,000

■ Machinery for £30,000

Calculate the maximum capital allowances that can be claimed, and insert the figures into the following sentences.

The AIA that can be claimed is   £

The writing down allowance that can be claimed at 20% is   £

The writing down allowance that can be claimed at 10% is   £

The total capital allowance that can be claimed is   £

The written down value carried forward is   £

6.5 A sole trader has the following tax-adjusted results for the tax years 2010/11 and 2011/12:

	2010/11	*2011/12*
Trading Profits	£20,000	£0
Other Income	£17,000	£28,000

The sole trader incurred a trading loss in 2011/12 of £44,000.

What is the maximum amount of the loss that could be set against the individual's income for 2010/11?

		✓
(a)	£20,000	
(b)	£37,000	
(c)	£44,000	
(d)	£16,000	
(e)	£0	

7 Chapter activities
Income tax – further issues

7.1 Clive started trading on 1 November 2010. He makes up his accounts to 31 December each year. The profits were calculated at:

	£
Period to 31 December 2010	16,000
Year to 31 December 2011	108,000
Year to 31 December 2012	92,000

(a) The tax year in which he started trading was (select one):

2008/09; 2009/10; 2010/11; 2011/12

(b) His taxable profits in his first tax year of trading were (select one):

£16,000; £43,000; £108,000; £124,000

(c) His taxable profits in his second tax year of trading were (select one):

£92,000; £97,000; £108,000; £124,000

(d) His taxable profits in his third tax year of trading were (select one):

£108,000; £124,000; £104,000; £92,000

(e) His overlap profits were £ [   ]

(f) His overlap profits are deducted (select one):

	✓
from his first year profits.	
from the profits in the second year of trading.	
from the profits in the third year of trading.	
from the profits in the final year of trading.	

7.2 An individual commences business as a sole trader on 1 February 2011. He makes his first set of accounts up to 30 April 2012, and thereafter to 30 April each year.

What is the basis period for the tax year 2011/12?

	✓
(a) 1 February 2011 to 30 April 2012	
(b) 1 May 2011 to 30 April 2012	
(c) 1 February 2011 to 31 January 2012	
(d) 6 April 2011 to 5 April 2012	
(e) 1 February 2011 to 5 April 2011	
(f) 1 February 2011 to 5 April 2012	

7.3 Pete and Heather have been in partnership for many years, running a fish smoking business, and sharing profits equally. They have always made their accounts up to 31 December each year.

On 1 September 2011, Ash joined the partnership and the profit sharing ratio was changed to 3:3:2 for Pete, Heather and Ash.

For the year ended 31 December 2011, the trading profit was £120,000.

(i) Using the following table, calculate the division of profits between the partners for the accounting year ended 31 December 2011.

	Total £	Pete £	Heather £	Ash £
1 Jan – 31 August 2011				
1 Sept – 31 Dec 2011				
Total				

(ii) What is the basis of assessment for 2011/12 for Ash?

	✓
(a) 1/9/2011 – 31/12/2011	
(b) 1/1/2011 – 31/12/2011	
(c) 1/9/2011 – 5/4/2012	
(d) 1/1/2012 – 5/4/2012	

7.4 Joe Salt's total income tax and Class 4 NIC for 2011/12 has been finalised as £11,600, all relating to his business as a sole trader. He made payments on account of £4,000 on each of 31 January 2012 and 31 July 2012 relating to 2011/12.

Using the following table, calculate the amounts of the payments that he needs to make on 31 January 2013 and 31 July 2013, assuming no claim to reduce payments is made.

		£
Payment on 31 January 2013	Balance of tax and NIC for 2011/12	
	Payment on account for 2012/13	
	Total	
Payment on 31 July 2013	Payment on account for 2012/13	

7.5 Deborah Baker commenced in business on 1 October 2011. She produced accounts for the year ended 30 September 2012, and the information from these accounts has been entered on the self-employment (full) pages (before tax adjustments).

The following items are included in the expenses shown in her accounts:

■ Wages and salaries includes her drawings of £20,000

■ Telephone costs include £400 for private calls

■ Bank charges include £530 interest on her credit card which is for personal use

■ Advertising includes entertaining customers costing £1,600, and a staff party costing £450

Deborah has also spent £29,000 on equipment and wishes to claim the maximum Annual Investment Allowance.

Required

Complete, as far as possible, the remainder of pages 1 to 3 of the full self employment supplementary pages that follow. (The 2010/11 form has been used as the 2011/12 version was not available when this book was published.)

Note that these pages relate to the accounting period, not the basis period. (The details relating to the basis period would be dealt with on supplementary page 4, but are not assessable.)

 **HM Revenue & Customs**

Self-employment (full)
Tax year 6 April 2010 to 5 April 2011

Read page SEFN 1 of the *notes* to check if you should use this page or the *Self-employment (short)* page.

Your name	Your Unique Taxpayer Reference (UTR)
Deborah Baker	

Business details

1 Business name – *unless it is in your own name*

2 Description of business

Trader

3 First line of your business address – *unless you work from home*

4 Postcode of your business address

5 If the details in boxes 1, 2, 3 or 4 have changed in the last 12 months, put 'X' in the box and give details in the 'Any other information' box

6 If your business started after 5 April 2010, enter the start date *DD MM YYYY*

`0 1  1 0  2 0 1 1`

7 If your business ceased after 5 April 2010 but before 6 April 2011, enter the final date of trading

8 Date your books or accounts start – *the beginning of your accounting period*

`0 1  1 0  2 0 1 1`

9 Date your books or accounts are made up to or the end of your accounting period – *read page SEFN 3 of the notes if you have filled in box 6 or 7*

`3 0  0 9  2 0 1 2`

Other information

10 If your accounting date has changed permanently, put 'X' in the box

11 If your accounting date has changed more than once since 2005, put 'X' in the box

12 If special arrangements apply, put 'X' in the box – *read page SEFN 4 of the notes*

13 If you provided the information about your 2010-11 profit on last year's tax return, put 'X' in the box – *read page SEFN 4 of the notes*

Business income

14 Your turnover – *the takings, fees, sales or money earned by your business*

£ `1 9 6 0 0 0 · 0 0`

15 Any other business income not included in box 14 – *excluding Business Start-up Allowance*

£ `· 0 0`

Business expenses

Read pages SEFN 7 to SEFN 9 of the *notes* before completing this section.

Total expenses

If your annual turnover was below £70,000 you may just put your total expenses in box 30

Disallowable expenses

Use this column if the figures in boxes 16 to 29 include disallowable amounts

	Total expenses		Disallowable expenses
16	Cost of goods bought for resale or goods used £ 5 8 5 0 0 · 0 0	31	£ · 0 0
17	Construction industry - *payments to subcontractors* £ · 0 0	32	£ · 0 0
18	Wages, salaries and other staff costs £ 4 3 8 0 0 · 0 0	33	£ · 0 0
19	Car, van and travel expenses £ · 0 0	34	£ · 0 0
20	Rent, rates, power and insurance costs £ 9 8 6 0 · 0 0	35	£ · 0 0
21	Repairs and renewals of property and equipment £ · 0 0	36	£ · 0 0
22	Phone, fax, stationery and other office costs £ 2 1 0 0 · 0 0	37	£ · 0 0
23	Advertising and business entertainment costs £ 3 0 4 0 · 0 0	38	£ · 0 0
24	Interest on bank and other loans £ · 0 0	39	£ · 0 0
25	Bank, credit card and other financial charges £ 1 5 0 0 · 0 0	40	£ · 0 0
26	Irrecoverable debts written off £ · 0 0	41	£ · 0 0
27	Accountancy, legal and other professional fees £ 2 0 0 0 · 0 0	42	£ · 0 0
28	Depreciation and loss/profit on sale of assets £ 2 9 0 0 · 0 0	43	£ · 0 0
29	Other business expenses £ · 0 0	44	£ · 0 0
30	Total expenses in boxes 16 to 29 £ 1 2 3 7 0 0 · 0 0	45	Total disallowable expenses in boxes 31 to 44 £ · 0 0

Net profit or loss

46 Net profit – *if your business income is more than your expenses (if box 14 + box 15 minus box 30 is positive)*

£ ⎣ ⎦⎣ ⎦⎣ 7 ⎦⎣ 2 ⎦⎣ 3 ⎦⎣ 0 ⎦⎣ 0 ⎦ · ⎣ 0 ⎦⎣ 0 ⎦

47 Or, net loss – *if your expenses are more than your business income (if box 30 minus (box 14 + box 15) is positive)*

£ ⎣ ⎦⎣ ⎦⎣ ⎦⎣ ⎦⎣ ⎦⎣ ⎦⎣ ⎦ · ⎣ 0 ⎦⎣ 0 ⎦

Tax allowances for vehicles and equipment (capital allowances)

There are 'capital' tax allowances for vehicles, equipment and certain buildings used in your business (you should not have included the cost of these in your business expenses). Read pages SEFN 10 to SEFN 15 of the *notes* and use the examples to work out your capital allowances.

48 Annual Investment Allowance

£ ⎣ ⎦⎣ ⎦⎣ ⎦⎣ ⎦⎣ ⎦⎣ ⎦⎣ ⎦ · ⎣ 0 ⎦⎣ 0 ⎦

49 Capital allowances at 20% on equipment, including cars with lower CO_2 emissions

£ ⎣ ⎦⎣ ⎦⎣ ⎦⎣ ⎦⎣ ⎦⎣ ⎦⎣ ⎦ · ⎣ 0 ⎦⎣ 0 ⎦

50 Capital allowances at 10% on equipment, including cars with higher CO_2 emissions

£ ⎣ ⎦⎣ ⎦⎣ ⎦⎣ ⎦⎣ ⎦⎣ ⎦⎣ ⎦ · ⎣ 0 ⎦⎣ 0 ⎦

51 Restricted capital allowances for cars costing more than £12,000 – *if bought before 6 April 2009*

£ ⎣ ⎦⎣ ⎦⎣ ⎦⎣ ⎦⎣ ⎦⎣ ⎦⎣ ⎦ · ⎣ 0 ⎦⎣ 0 ⎦

52 Agricultural or Industrial Buildings Allowance

£ ⎣ ⎦⎣ ⎦⎣ ⎦⎣ ⎦⎣ ⎦⎣ ⎦⎣ ⎦ · ⎣ 0 ⎦⎣ 0 ⎦

53 Business Premises Renovation Allowance (Assisted Areas only) – *read page SEFN 13 of the notes*

£ ⎣ ⎦⎣ ⎦⎣ ⎦⎣ ⎦⎣ ⎦⎣ ⎦⎣ ⎦ · ⎣ 0 ⎦⎣ 0 ⎦

54 100% and other enhanced capital allowances – *read page SEFN 13 of the notes*

£ ⎣ ⎦⎣ ⎦⎣ ⎦⎣ ⎦⎣ ⎦⎣ ⎦⎣ ⎦ · ⎣ 0 ⎦⎣ 0 ⎦

55 Allowances on sale or cessation of business use (where you have disposed of assets for less than their tax value)

£ ⎣ ⎦⎣ ⎦⎣ ⎦⎣ ⎦⎣ ⎦⎣ ⎦⎣ ⎦ · ⎣ 0 ⎦⎣ 0 ⎦

56 Total allowances (total of boxes 48 to 55)

£ ⎣ ⎦⎣ ⎦⎣ ⎦⎣ ⎦⎣ ⎦⎣ ⎦⎣ ⎦ · ⎣ 0 ⎦⎣ 0 ⎦

57 Balancing charge on sale or cessation of business use (only where Business Premises Renovation Allowance has been claimed)

£ ⎣ ⎦⎣ ⎦⎣ ⎦⎣ ⎦⎣ ⎦⎣ ⎦⎣ ⎦ · ⎣ 0 ⎦⎣ 0 ⎦

58 Balancing charge on sales of other assets or on the cessation of business use (where you have disposed of assets for more than their tax value)

£ ⎣ ⎦⎣ ⎦⎣ ⎦⎣ ⎦⎣ ⎦⎣ ⎦⎣ ⎦ · ⎣ 0 ⎦⎣ 0 ⎦

Calculating your taxable profit or loss

You may have to adjust your net profit or loss for disallowable expenses or capital allowances to arrive at your taxable profit or your loss for tax purposes. Read pages SEFN 15 and SEFN 16 of the *notes* and fill in the boxes below that apply.

59 Goods and services for your own use – *read page SEFN 15 of the notes*

£ ⎣ ⎦⎣ ⎦⎣ ⎦⎣ ⎦⎣ ⎦⎣ ⎦⎣ ⎦ · ⎣ 0 ⎦⎣ 0 ⎦

60 Total additions to net profit or deductions from net loss (box 45 + box 57 + box 58 + box 59)

£ ⎣ ⎦⎣ ⎦⎣ ⎦⎣ ⎦⎣ ⎦⎣ ⎦⎣ ⎦ · ⎣ 0 ⎦⎣ 0 ⎦

61 Income, receipts and other profits included in business income or expenses but not taxable as business profits

£ ⎣ ⎦⎣ ⎦⎣ ⎦⎣ ⎦⎣ ⎦⎣ ⎦⎣ ⎦ · ⎣ 0 ⎦⎣ 0 ⎦

62 Total deductions from net profit or additions to net loss (box 56 + box 61)

£ ⎣ ⎦⎣ ⎦⎣ ⎦⎣ ⎦⎣ ⎦⎣ ⎦⎣ ⎦ · ⎣ 0 ⎦⎣ 0 ⎦

63 Net business profit for tax purposes (if box 46 + box 60 minus (box 47 + box 62) is positive)

£ ⎣ ⎦⎣ ⎦⎣ ⎦⎣ ⎦⎣ ⎦⎣ ⎦⎣ ⎦ · ⎣ 0 ⎦⎣ 0 ⎦

64 Net business loss for tax purposes (if box 47 + box 62 minus (box 46 + box 60) is positive)

£ ⎣ ⎦⎣ ⎦⎣ ⎦⎣ ⎦⎣ ⎦⎣ ⎦⎣ ⎦ · ⎣ 0 ⎦⎣ 0 ⎦

8 Chapter activities
Capital Gains Tax for individuals

8.1 Select the appropriate procedure for a capital gains tax computation of an individual by ticking the appropriate column. Assume that there is no claim for gift relief where appropriate.

✓

	Use Actual Proceeds	Use market value for proceeds	No gain or loss basis
Sale of asset for £5,000 to a friend. Market value of asset is £20,000.			
Gift of asset to friend. Market value of asset is £20,000.			
Sale of asset to business partner's wife for £5,000. Market value of asset is £20,000.			
Gift of asset to civil partner. Market value of asset is £20,000.			
Sale of asset to business partner's grandson for £5,000. Market value of asset is £20,000.			
Sale of business asset to an unconnected limited company.			
Sale of asset to husband for £20,000. Market value of asset is £5,000.			

8.2 Adam purchased and sold shares in Beeco Limited as follows:

- 15 April 2005   Purchased 5,600 shares for £14,560
- 12 January 2012   Sold 1,400 shares for £4,060
- 1 February 2012   Purchased 2,800 shares for £6,160
- 31 March 2012   Sold 7,000 shares for £20,000

(a) The gain or loss on the sale of shares on 12 January 2012 is

£ _____ gain / loss.

(b) The gain or loss on the sale of shares on 31 March 2012 is

£ _____ gain / loss

8.3 Poppy Price is a sole trader. She purchased a warehouse in October 2002 for £280,000, and sold it in April 2011 for £430,000. She purchased a shop in October 2011 for £390,000.

(a) Complete the following table relating to the gain on the sale of the warehouse, and any deferral of that gain. This was her only capital gain in 2011/12.

	£
Sale proceeds	
Cost	
Total gain	
Deferred gain	
Gain chargeable immediately	
Annual exempt amount	
Amount subject to CGT	

(b) The cost of the shop will be deemed to be £ [   ] when it is ultimately sold.

8.4 The following statements relate to entrepreneurs' relief. State whether the statements are true or false.

✓

	True	False
(a) It is subject to a lifetime limit of £10,000,000 per individual.		
(b) It works by charging the gain at 8%.		
(c) All disposals made by an individual are eligible.		
(d) It can relate to the disposal of shares held in a 'personal trading company'.		
(e) It is subject to a lifetime limit of £100,000,000.		
(f) It works by charging the gain at 10%.		
(g) It effectively uses up the basic rate band so other gains that are not eligible are more likely to be taxed at 28%.		

8.5 There are similarities and differences between chargeable gains for companies subject to Corporation Tax, and Capital Gains Tax for individuals.

Select the rules and reliefs that apply to either or both companies and individuals by ticking the appropriate columns in the following table.

✓

	Companies (Corporation Tax)	Individuals (Capital Gains Tax)
Gift relief		
Rollover relief		
Annual exempt amount		
Indexation allowance		
Chattel rules		
Entrepreneurs' relief		
Part disposal rules		

Answers to chapter activities

1

Chapter activities

Introduction to business taxation

1.1   (a), (c) and (e) are correct.

1.2

	Period return relates to	Latest return submission date	Latest tax payment date
Corporation Tax	Chargeable accounting period	12 months after end of period that accounts are based on	9 months and one day after end of chargeable accounting period
Income Tax	Tax year	31 January following tax year	31 January following tax year

1.3   (1)   £35,250

(2)   £3,223.00

1.4   (a), (b), (c) and (d) are true; (e) and (f) are false.

1.5   The final submission dates for tax returns are as follows:

A sole trader with accounts made up to 31 March 2012: 31 January 2013

A sole trader with accounts made up to 30 June 2012: 31 January 2014

A limited company with accounts made up to 31 December 2011: 31 December 2012

2 Chapter activities
Corporation tax – trading profits

2.1

	Add to net profit	Deduct from net profit	No adjustment required
Depreciation	✓		
Discount received			✓
Directors' salaries			✓
Dividends received		✓	
Rent receivable		✓	
Rent payable			✓
Interest payable			✓
Advertising costs			✓
Entertaining customers	✓		

2.2 The adjusted trading profit (before capital allowances) is

(c)   £40,000   *(£37,000 - £12,000 + £13,000 + £2,000)*

2.3 (a), (d) and (g) are true; (b), (c), (e) and (f) are false.

2.4 (e) shows the correct approach.

2.5 The maximum amount of loss that could be set against the taxable total profits tax for 2010 is

(a) £56,000 *(the loss must first be set against the £25,000 investment income and gains of 2011 before it can be carried back to the previous year)*

3 Chapter activities
Corporation tax – capital allowances

3.1

	Qualifying	Not qualifying
Car for employee's private use	✓	
Office furniture	✓	
Capital expenditure on software	✓	
Payments for vehicle on operating lease		✓
Vehicles bought on credit	✓	
Buildings		✓
Equipment bought through hire purchase	✓	

3.2 The AIA that can be claimed is £60,000

The first year allowance that can be claimed at 100% is £26,000

The writing down allowance that can be claimed at 20% is £0

The writing down allowance that can be claimed at 10% is £2,200

The total capital allowance that can be claimed is £88,200

3.3

	AIA (to limit)	20% WDA Main Pool	10% WDA Special Rate Pool	100% FYA
Car emissions of 185 g/km			✓	
Car emissions of 99 g/km				✓
Machinery	✓			
Zero-emission goods vehicle				✓
Car emissions of 135 g/km		✓		
Water-efficient plant				✓

3.4   (b) and (d) are true; (a), (c) and (e) are false.

3.5   **Capital Allowance Computation**

	main pool £	exp car Saab £	exp car BMW £	special rate pool £	capital allowances £
WDV bf	120,000	19,000	16,000		
add					
Acquisitions					
without FYA or AIA:					
Car (190g/km)				35,000	
Acquisitions					
qualifying for AIA					
Machinery £105,500					
AIA £(100,000)					100,000
Excess	5,500				
less					
Proceeds of disposals:	(5,000)		(7,000)		
	120,500	19,000	9,000	35,000	
20% WDA	(24,100)	(3,000)			27,100
10% WDA				(3,500)	3,500
Balancing Allowance			(9,000)		9,000
WDV cf	96,400	16,000	0	31,500	
Total Capital Allowances					139,600

4 Chapter activities
Corporation tax – chargeable gains

4.1

	Actual Proceeds	Market Value	£6,000	Zero
Sale of asset for £15,000 to Director who owns 80% of shares in company. Market value of asset is £35,000.		✓		
Gift of asset to unconnected individual (non-shareholder).		✓		
Sale of asset to company employee (non-shareholder) at below market value.	✓			
Sale of chattel for £4,000 (its market value) that had originally cost £10,000.			✓	
Destruction of an uninsured asset during fire.				✓
Sale of asset for £15,000 to Director who owns 10% of shares in company. Market value of asset is £35,000.	✓			
Shares owned in an unconnected company that have become worthless due to the company's liquidation.				✓

4.2   Proceeds: £10,000

Cost: £3,500

Indexation allowance: £1,327

Gain: £5,173

Chattel restriction on gain: £6,667

The chattel restriction will NOT have any effect on the original gain.

4.3

	No. Shares	Cost £	Indexed Cost £
Purchase	8,000	19,500	19,500
Index to July 2003			2,223
Rights issue	200	360	360
Sub total	8,200	19,860	22,083
Index to June 2011			6,559
Sub total	8,200	19,860	28,642
Disposal	(6,000)	(14,532)	(20,958)
Pool balance	2,200	5,328	**7,684**

Proceeds	£24,000
Indexed Cost	£20,958
Gain	£3,042

4.4   Proceeds: £40,000

Cost[1]: £36,000

Indexation allowance: £13,644

Gain or (Loss)[2]: £0

Notes:

(1)   *Cost is calculated as £90,000 x £40,000 / (£40,000 + £60,000)*

(2)   *Indexation cannot create a loss*

4.5   Proceeds[1]: £6,000

Cost: £7,500

Indexation allowance[2]: £0

Gain or (Loss): (£1,500)

Notes:

(1)   *Deemed proceeds are £6,000 for a chattel sold at a loss for under £6,000*

(2)   *Indexation allowance cannot be used to increase a loss*

5 Chapter activities

Corporation tax – calculating the tax

5.1

	£
Corporation Tax at Main Rate	182,000
Marginal Relief	10,500
Corporation Tax Payable	171,500

Marginal Relief working:

3/200 x (1,500,000 – 750,000) x (700,000 / 750,000) = £10,500

5.2

	£
Maximum of Band	500,000
Corporation Tax at Main Rate	93,600
Marginal Relief	2,100
Corporation Tax Payable	91,500

Marginal relief working:

3/200 x (500,000 – 360,000) x 1 = £2,100

5.3

Loss	**Rules that can apply**
Trading Loss	(e)
Capital Loss	(f)
Rental Loss	(a)

5.4 See completed form, opposite.

5.5 (b), (c), (e), (f) and (g) are true; (a) and (d) are false.

5.4 Page 2

Company tax calculation

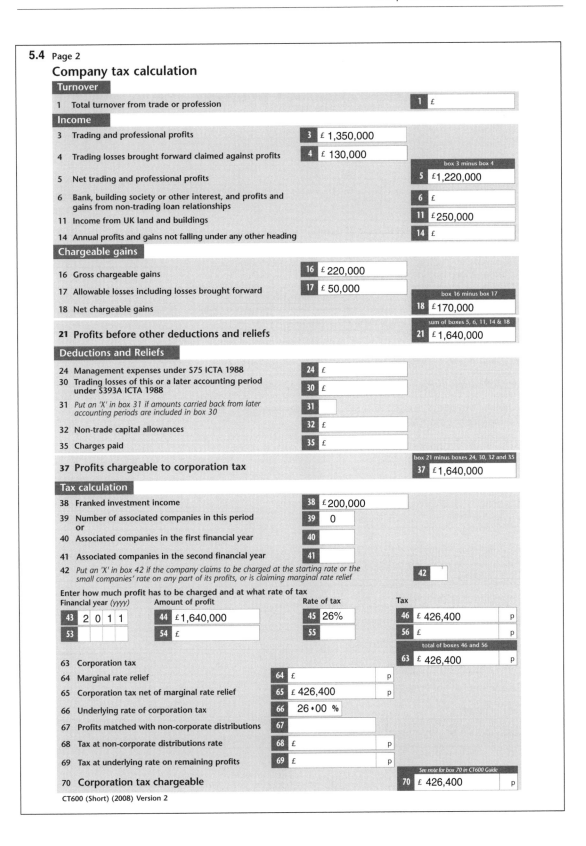

Turnover

1   Total turnover from trade or profession   **1** £

Income

3   Trading and professional profits   **3** £ 1,350,000

4   Trading losses brought forward claimed against profits   **4** £ 130,000

| | | box 3 minus box 4 |
5   Net trading and professional profits   **5** £1,220,000

6   Bank, building society or other interest, and profits and gains from non-trading loan relationships   **6** £

11   Income from UK land and buildings   **11** £250,000

14   Annual profits and gains not falling under any other heading   **14** £

Chargeable gains

16   Gross chargeable gains   **16** £ 220,000

17   Allowable losses including losses brought forward   **17** £ 50,000

box 16 minus box 17
18   Net chargeable gains   **18** £170,000

sum of boxes 5, 6, 11, 14 & 18
21   Profits before other deductions and reliefs   **21** £ 1,640,000

Deductions and Reliefs

24   Management expenses under S75 ICTA 1988   **24** £

30   Trading losses of this or a later accounting period under S393A ICTA 1988   **30** £

31   Put an 'X' in box 31 if amounts carried back from later accounting periods are included in box 30   **31**

32   Non-trade capital allowances   **32** £

35   Charges paid   **35** £

box 21 minus boxes 24, 30, 32 and 35
37   Profits chargeable to corporation tax   **37** £1,640,000

Tax calculation

38   Franked investment income   **38** £200,000

39   Number of associated companies in this period or   **39** 0

40   Associated companies in the first financial year   **40**

41   Associated companies in the second financial year   **41**

42   Put an 'X' in box 42 if the company claims to be charged at the starting rate or the small companies' rate on any part of its profits, or is claiming marginal rate relief   **42**

Enter how much profit has to be charged and at what rate of tax

Financial year *(yyyy)*	Amount of profit	Rate of tax	Tax
43 2 0 1 1	**44** £1,640,000	**45** 26%	**46** £ 426,400 p
53	**54** £	**55**	**56** £ p

total of boxes 46 and 56
63 £ 426,400   p

63   Corporation tax

64   Marginal rate relief   **64** £   p

65   Corporation tax net of marginal rate relief   **65** £ 426,400   p

66   Underlying rate of corporation tax   **66** 26•00 %

67   Profits matched with non-corporate distributions   **67**

68   Tax at non-corporate distributions rate   **68** £   p

69   Tax at underlying rate on remaining profits   **69** £   p

See note for box 70 in CT600 Guide
70   Corporation tax chargeable   **70** £ 426,400   p

CT600 (Short) (2008) Version 2

6

Chapter activities
Income tax – trading profits

6.1

	Badges of Trade
Reason for acquisition and sale of item(s)	✓
Whether individual enjoys carrying out the activity	
Whether there is a profit motive	✓
How long the individual has owned the item(s) before sale	✓
Whether the individual only sells via computer sites	
Whether any supplementary work is carried out on the item(s) before sale	✓
Whether the individual considers the activity to be his hobby	
How often the individual carries out similar transactions	✓
Whether the items bought and sold (the subject matter) are used personally by the individual before sale	✓

6.2

	Allowable expenditure	Non-allowable expenditure
Cost of sales	✓	
Entertaining staff	✓	
Fines for lawbreaking by business owner		✓
Gifts of food or drink to customers		✓
Trade bad debts written off	✓	
Salary and NIC of business owner		✓
Depreciation		✓
Loss on sale of non-current assets		✓

6.3

	£	£
Net Profit		112,310
Add		
Goods for own use	2,000	
Depreciation	22,020	
Laura's salary	45,000	
Laura's son's salary (unreasonable)	28,000	
Gifts of bottles of wine	2,400	
Laura's son's car expenses	3,800	
Increase in general bad debt provision	2,600	
		105,820
		218,130
Less		
Capital allowances		10,400
Adjusted trading profits		207,730

6.4   The AIA that can be claimed is £44,400[1]

The writing down allowance that can be claimed at 20% is £2,400[2]

The writing down allowance that can be claimed at 10% is £0

The total capital allowance that can be claimed is £46,800[3]

The written down value carried forward is £16,000[4]

Workings:

(1)   *£30,000 + (£18,000 x 80%) = £44,400*

(2)   *£20,000 x 20% x 60% = £2,400*

(3)   *£44,400 + £2,400 = £46,800*

(4)   *£20,000 – (£20,000 x 20%) = £16,000*

6.5   (b)   £37,000

The rules for a sole trader or partnership mean that the loss can be set off against the previous year's total income without first setting off in the current year.

7 Chapter activities
Income tax – further issues

7.1 **(a)** The tax year in which he started trading was 2010/11.

(b) His taxable profits in his first tax year of trading were £43,000.

(c) His taxable profits in his second tax year of trading were £108,000.

(d) His taxable profits in his third tax year of trading were £92,000.

(e) His overlap profits were £27,000.

(f) His overlap profits are deducted from the profits in the final year of trading.

7.2 **(d)** 6 April 2011 to 5 April 2012

7.3 **(i)**

	Total	Pete	Heather	Ash
	£	£	£	£
1 Jan – 31 August 2011	80,000	40,000	40,000	0
1 Sept – 31 Dec 2011	40,000	15,000	15,000	10,000
Total	120,000	55,000	55,000	10,000

(ii) **(c)** 1/9/2011 – 5/4/2012

7.4

		£
Payment on 31 January 2013	Balance of tax and NIC for 2011/12	3,600
	Payment on account for 2012/13	5,800
	Total	9,400
Payment on 31 July 2013	Payment on account for 2012/13	5,800

7.5

HM Revenue & Customs

Self-employment (full)

Tax year 6 April 2010 to 5 April 2011

Read page SEFN 1 of the *notes* to check if you should use this page or the *Self-employment (short)* page.

Your name	Your Unique Taxpayer Reference (UTR)
Deborah Baker	

Business details

1 Business name - *unless it is in your own name*

2 Description of business

Trader

3 First line of your business address - *unless you work from home*

4 Postcode of your business address

5 If the details in boxes 1, 2, 3 or 4 have changed in the last 12 months, put 'X' in the box and give details in the 'Any other information' box

6 If your business started after 5 April 2010, enter the start date *DD MM YYYY*

0 1 1 0 2 0 1 1

7 If your business ceased after 5 April 2010 but before 6 April 2011, enter the final date of trading

8 Date your books or accounts start - *the beginning of your accounting period*

0 1 1 0 2 0 1 1

9 Date your books or accounts are made up to or the end of your accounting period - *read page SEFN 3 of the notes if you have filled in box 6 or 7*

3 0 0 9 2 0 1 2

Other information

10 If your accounting date has changed permanently, put 'X' in the box

11 If your accounting date has changed more than once since 2005, put 'X' in the box

12 If special arrangements apply, put 'X' in the box - *read page SEFN 4 of the notes*

13 If you provided the information about your 2010-11 profit on last year's tax return, put 'X' in the box - *read page SEFN 4 of the notes*

Business income

14 Your turnover - *the takings, fees, sales or money earned by your business*

£ 1 9 6 0 0 0 . 0 0

15 Any other business income not included in box 14 - *excluding Business Start-up Allowance*

£ . 0 0

SA103F 2011   Tax return: Self-employment (full): Page SEF 1   HMRC 12/10

Business expenses

Read pages SEFN 7 to SEFN 9 of the *notes* before completing this section.

Total expenses
If your annual turnover was below £70,000 you may just put your total expenses in box 30

Disallowable expenses
Use this column if the figures in boxes 16 to 29 include disallowable amounts

	Total expenses		Disallowable expenses
16	Cost of goods bought for resale or goods used	31	
	£ 58 500 · 0 0		£ · 0 0
17	Construction industry - *payments to subcontractors*	32	
	£ · 0 0		£ · 0 0
18	Wages, salaries and other staff costs	33	
	£ 43 800 · 0 0		£ 20 000 · 0 0
19	Car, van and travel expenses	34	
	£ · 0 0		£ · 0 0
20	Rent, rates, power and insurance costs	35	
	£ 9 860 · 0 0		£ · 0 0
21	Repairs and renewals of property and equipment	36	
	£ · 0 0		£ · 0 0
22	Phone, fax, stationery and other office costs	37	
	£ 2 100 · 0 0		£ 400 · 0 0
23	Advertising and business entertainment costs	38	
	£ 3 040 · 0 0		£ 1 600 · 0 0
24	Interest on bank and other loans	39	
	£ · 0 0		£ · 0 0
25	Bank, credit card and other financial charges	40	
	£ 1 500 · 0 0		£ 530 · 0 0
26	Irrecoverable debts written off	41	
	£ · 0 0		£ · 0 0
27	Accountancy, legal and other professional fees	42	
	£ 2 000 · 0 0		£ · 0 0
28	Depreciation and loss/profit on sale of assets	43	
	£ 2 900 · 0 0		£ 2 900 · 0 0
29	Other business expenses	44	
	£ · 0 0		£ · 0 0
30	Total expenses in boxes 16 to 29	45	Total disallowable expenses in boxes 31 to 44
	£ 123 700 · 0 0		£ 25 430 · 0 0

Net profit or loss

46	Net profit – *if your business income is more than your expenses (if box 14 + box 15 minus box 30 is positive)*

£   7 2 3 0 0 · 0 0

47	Or, net loss – *if your expenses are more than your business income (if box 30 minus (box 14 + box 15) is positive)*

£   · 0 0

Tax allowances for vehicles and equipment (capital allowances)

There are 'capital' tax allowances for vehicles, equipment and certain buildings used in your business (you should not have included the cost of these in your business expenses). Read pages SEFN 10 to SEFN 15 of the *notes* and use the examples to work out your capital allowances.

48	Annual Investment Allowance

£   2 9 0 0 0 · 0 0

49	Capital allowances at 20% on equipment, including cars with lower CO_2 emissions

£   · 0 0

50	Capital allowances at 10% on equipment, including cars with higher CO_2 emissions

£   · 0 0

51	Restricted capital allowances for cars costing more than £12,000 – *if bought before 6 April 2009*

£   · 0 0

52	Agricultural or Industrial Buildings Allowance

£   · 0 0

53	Business Premises Renovation Allowance (Assisted Areas only) – *read page SEFN 13 of the notes*

£   · 0 0

54	100% and other enhanced capital allowances – *read page SEFN 13 of the notes*

£   · 0 0

55	Allowances on sale or cessation of business use (where you have disposed of assets for less than their tax value)

£   · 0 0

56	Total allowances (total of boxes 48 to 55)

£   2 9 0 0 0 · 0 0

57	Balancing charge on sale or cessation of business use (only where Business Premises Renovation Allowance has been claimed)

£   · 0 0

58	Balancing charge on sales of other assets or on the cessation of business use (where you have disposed of assets for more than their tax value)

£   · 0 0

Calculating your taxable profit or loss

You may have to adjust your net profit or loss for disallowable expenses or capital allowances to arrive at your taxable profit or your loss for tax purposes. Read pages SEFN 15 and SEFN 16 of the *notes* and fill in the boxes below that apply.

59	Goods and services for your own use – *read page SEFN 15 of the notes*

£   · 0 0

60	Total additions to net profit or deductions from net loss (box 45 + box 57 + box 58 + box 59)

£   2 5 4 3 0 · 0 0

61	Income, receipts and other profits included in business income or expenses but not taxable as business profits

£   · 0 0

62	Total deductions from net profit or additions to net loss (box 56 + box 61)

£   2 9 0 0 0 · 0 0

63	Net business profit for tax purposes (if box 46 + box 60 minus (box 47 + box 62) is positive)

£   6 8 7 3 0 · 0 0

64	Net business loss for tax purposes (if box 47 + box 62 minus (box 46 + box 60) is positive)

£   · 0 0

8 Chapter activities

Capital Gains Tax for individuals

8.1

	Use Actual Proceeds	Use market value for proceeds	No gain or loss basis
Sale of asset for £5,000 to a friend. Market value of asset is £20,000.	✓		
Gift of asset to friend. Market value of asset is £20,000.		✓	
Sale of asset to business partner's wife for £5,000. Market value of asset is £20,000.		✓	
Gift of asset to civil partner. Market value of asset is £20,000.			✓
Sale of asset to business partner's grandson for £5,000. Market value of asset is £20,000.		✓	
Sale of business asset to an unconnected limited company.	✓		
Sale of asset to husband for £20,000. Market value of asset is £5,000.			✓

8.2 **(a)** The **gain** on the sale of shares on 12 January 2012 is £980.

The shares sold on 12 January are matched with 1,400 of those bought on 1 February (within the following 30 days), leaving 1,400 of that purchase unmatched.

(b) The **gain** on the sale of shares on 31 March 2012 is £2,360.

The shares sold on 31 March are matched with the pooled purchases of 5,600 + 1,400 (balance) = 7,000 shares, costing a total of £17,640.

8.3   **(a)**

	£
Sale proceeds	430,000
Cost	280,000
Total gain	150,000
Deferred gain	110,000
Gain chargeable immediately	40,000
Annual exempt amount	10,600
Amount subject to CGT	29,400

(b)   The cost of the shop will be deemed to be £280,000 when it is ultimately sold.
(£390,000 - £110,000).

8.4   (a), (d), (f) and (g) are true; (b), (c) and (e) are false.

8.5

	Companies (Corporation Tax)	Individuals (Capital Gains Tax)
Gift relief		✓
Rollover relief	✓	✓
Annual exempt amount		✓
Indexation allowance	✓	
Chattel rules	✓	✓
Entrepreneurs' relief		✓
Part disposal rules	✓	✓

Business taxation

Practice assessment 1

Section 1

Task 1.1

Analyse the following expenditure into capital and revenue by ticking the appropriate column.

✓

	Capital	Revenue
Repairs to factory roof		
Computer software costing £10,000		
Insurance premiums		
Second hand van		

Task 1.2

Lesley Lampeter is a sole trader. Her business has the following income statement:

	£	£
Turnover		1,150,000
Cost of sales		758,450
Gross profit		391,550
Wages and salaries	112,510	
Rent, rates and insurance	40,350	
Advertising and entertaining	11,585	
Professional fees	5,060	
Motor expenses	50,030	
Telephone and office costs	33,050	
Depreciation	22,680	
Other expenses	30,310	305,575
Net Profit		85,975

Notes:

1. Lesley took goods from the business that cost £1,000 and would normally sell for £1,750. The cost has already been excluded from cost of sales.

2. Wages and salaries include: £

   Lesley's class 2 NIC contributions   130

   Lesley's pension contributions   7,995

3. Advertising and entertaining includes: £

   Gifts to customers:

       Bottles of whisky costing £28 each   2,800

       400 calendars carrying the business's logo   1,200

4. Professional fees include: £

   Costs incurred in tax appeal   2,500

5. Motor expenses include: £

   Lesley's car expenses (used 50% for business)   3,900

6. Other expenses include: £

   Bad debts written off   1,450

   Increase in specific bad debt provision   2,000

7. Capital allowances have already been calculated at £20,680

Complete the adjusted trading profits computation.

Task 1.3

Cherie started trading on 1 October 2010. She makes up her accounts to 31 December. The profits were calculated as:

	£
Period to 31 December 2011	120,000
Year to 31 December 2012	84,000
Year to 31 December 2013	99,000

(a) The tax year in which she started trading was *(select one)*:

2008/09; 2009/10; 2010/11; 2011/12

(b) Her taxable profits in her first tax year of trading were *(select one)*:

£24,000; £48,000; £96,000; £120,000

(c) Her taxable profits in her second tax year of trading were *(select one)*:

£84,000; £96,000; £99,000; £120,000

(d) Her taxable profits in her third tax year of trading were *(select one)*:

£84,000; £87,750; £93,000; £99,000

(e) Her overlap profits were £

Task 1.4

A sole trader has the following tax-adjusted results for the tax years 2010/11 and 2011/12:

	2010/11	*2011/12*
Trading Profits	£12,000	£0
Other Income	£19,000	£21,000

The sole trader incurred a trading loss in 2011/12 of £38,000.

Which one of the following statements shows the full options for the amount of the loss that could be set against the individual's income for 2010/11?

✓

(a) any amount up to £31,000	
(b) any amount up to £17,000	
(c) any amount up to £19,000	
(d) either £12,000 or nothing	
(e) either £31,000 or £17,000 or nothing	
(f) either £17,000 or nothing	
(g) either £17,000 or £12,000 or nothing	
(h) £0 only	

Task 1.5

Ivor, Jo and Kirsty have been in partnership for many years, sharing profits in the ratio 5:3:2. They have always made their accounts up to 31 December each year.

On 31 July 2011, Kirsty decided to leave the partnership. The remaining partners then agreed to divide their profits equally.

For the year ended 31 December 2010, the partnership trading profit was £96,000.

For the year ended 31 December 2011, the partnership trading profit was £120,000.

Kirsty had no overlap profits brought forward.

(i) Using the following table, calculate the division of profits between the partners for the accounting year ended 31 December 2011.

	Total	Ivor	Jo	Kirsty
	£	£	£	£
1 Jan – 31 July 2011				
1 Aug – 31 Dec 2011				
Total				

(ii) What is the trading assessment for 2011/12 for Kirsty?

£

Task 1.6

Delta Limited has produced the following results for the 16-month accounting period to 31 December 2011.

Trading Profits for 16-month period (before capital allowances)	£800,000
Capital Allowances: y/e 31/8/2011	£54,000
4 months to 31/12/2011	£19,000
Chargeable Gains: Disposal 12/12/2010	£36,000
Disposal 19/4/2011	£14,000
Disposal 10/10/2011	£41,000
Rental Income – monthly amount	£2,000
Gift Aid Payment (paid 31/12/2011)	£6,000

Use the following table to calculate the TTP for each CAP.

	CAP 12 months to 31/8/2011 £	CAP 4 months to 31/12/2011 £
Trading Profits before CAs		
Capital Allowances		
Trading Profits		
Chargeable Gains		
Rental Income		
Sub total		
Gift Aid		
TTP		

Task 1.7

A company has the following information regarding its non-current assets for a 12-month CAP, ending on 30/6/2011.

	£
Written down values brought forward:	
General (main) pool	105,000
Finance Director's car (80% business use) Ford	17,000
Additions:	
Computer System	90,000
New car for Sales Director (emissions 99 g/km)	25,000
Disposals:	
Machinery	5,000

Calculate the maximum capital allowances for the CAP.

Section 2

Task 2.1

Analyse the following assets into those that are chargeable regarding CGT and those that are exempt.

✓

	Chargeable	Exempt
Government Stocks (gilts)		
Shares in Limited Companies		
Trading Inventory		
Land		

Task 2.2

Trolley Ltd sold an antique painting for £7,100 in June 2011. This was bought for £4,000 in August 2000. The indexation factor from August 2000 to June 2011 was 0.379.

Complete the following computation:

Proceeds £

Cost £

Indexation allowance £

Gain £

Chattel restriction on gain £

State whether the chattel restriction will have any effect on the original gain. yes/no

Task 2.3

Perfect Ltd bought 9,000 shares in Toronto Ltd for £27,900 in October 2001. Bonus shares were issued in April 2002 at 1 for 10. Purchases of 5,000 shares were made in July 2003 for £3.80 per share. In June 2011, Perfect Ltd sold 10,000 of the shares for £4.50 per share.

Indexation factors were:

October 2001 to July 2003:	0.114
July 2003 to June 2011:	0.297

Calculate the pool balances remaining and the gain made on the share disposal.

	No. Shares	Cost £	Indexed Cost £

Proceeds	£
Indexed Cost	£
Gain	£

Task 2.4

Select from the following statements, those that are true.　✓

		True	False
(a)	Entrepreneurs' relief is subject to a limit of £1,000,000 per transaction.		
(b)	Entrepreneurs' relief results in eligible gains being effectively taxed at 12%.		
(c)	Entrepreneurs' relief can be claimed by both companies and individuals.		
(d)	If an individual gives a business asset to another individual and both agree, they can claim gift relief to defer the gain.		
(e)	Gift relief is only available for spouses, civil partners, and connected persons.		
(f)	If Mary gives a business asset that cost £5,000 to Mike and they claim gift relief, the asset will have a base value of £5,000 when Mike disposes of it later.		

Task 2.5

Polly Prince is a sole trader. She purchased a warehouse in October 2000 for £180,000, and sold it in September 2011 for £400,000. She had purchased a shop in October 2010 for £335,000. The disposal of the warehouse is eligible for entrepreneurs' relief. Polly has not previously made any claims for entrepreneurs' relief.

(a) Complete the following table relating to the gain on the sale of the warehouse, and deferral of that gain (if any). This was her only capital gain in 2011/12.

	£
Sale proceeds	
Cost	
Total gain	
Deferred gain	
Gain chargeable immediately	
Annual exempt amount	
Capital Gains Tax payable	

(b) The cost of the shop will be deemed to be £ ⬚ when it is ultimately sold.

Task 2.6

Carol purchased and sold shares in Ceeco Limited as follows:

10 April 2002	Purchased 5,000 shares for £15,000
12 January 2012	Sold 1,800 shares for £4,000
1 February 2012	Purchased 6,800 shares for £21,080
31 March 2012	Sold 10,000 shares for £40,000

(a) The gain or loss on the sale of shares on 12 January 2012 is

£ [   ] gain / loss.

(b) The gain or loss on the sale of shares on 31 March 2012 is

£ [   ] gain / loss

Task 2.7

Which of the following statements are correct?   ✓

(a)	Every self employed taxpayer must pay Class 2 NIC, unless the profits are more than £42,475.	
(b)	Class 4 NIC is payable by the self employed at 9% on profits between £7,225 and £42,475.	
(c)	Class 4 NIC is payable at 2% on any drawings over £42,475.	
(d)	Class 4 NIC is subject to the same system of payment as income tax for sole traders.	
(e)	Class 4 NIC is payable at 2% for profits over £42,475.	
(f)	Class 2 NIC may be paid monthly by direct debit.	

Task 2.8

Enter the appropriate dates for payment of tax by individuals.

Payment type	Date
First instalment for 2011/12	
Second instalment for 2011/12	
Final balance for 2011/12	
First instalment for 2012/13	
Second instalment for 2012/13	
CGT for 2011/12	

Task 2.9

Gamma Ltd is a trading company with two associated companies. It has the following results for the 6 month CAP to 31/12/2011.

	£
Trading Profits	130,000
Chargeable Gains	25,000
Gift Aid Payments	15,000

Calculate the corporation tax using the following table.

	£
Maximum of Band	
Minimum of Band	
Corporation Tax at Main Rate	
Marginal Relief	
Corporation Tax Payable	

Task 2.10

From the following statements relating to companies, select those that are true.   ✓

		True	False
(a)	Companies must inform HMRC within 3 months that they have started trading. The penalty is between 0% and 100% of the 'potential lost revenue'.		
(b)	Where a Corporation Tax Return is submitted over 12 months late a percentage penalty of 10% of the Corporation Tax applies.		
(c)	Interest is charged on late payments (including instalments). Interest is also paid where there are early payments, but at a lower rate.		
(d)	Errors in tax returns caused by a lack of reasonable care can suffer a penalty of between 0% and 100% of the extra tax due.		
(e)	Failure to keep records can result in a penalty of £10,000 per chargeable accounting period.		
(f)	Errors in tax returns that are both deliberate and concealed are subject to a penalty of up to 100% of the extra tax due.		
(g)	Records need to be kept for at least 7 years from the end of the accounting period.		

Task 2.11

Alison Amsterdam and Bob Bolton have been trading in partnership for many years with accounting year ends of 31 March. They trade in wholesale fabric. The trade profits and taxed interest received are both divided between the partners in the ratio 3:2.

In the accounting year ended 31/3/2012, the partnership had trade profits of £80,000 and received taxed interest of £2,000.

Complete page 6 of the partnership tax return (the 2010/11 version is reproduced on the next page) relating to

■   the whole partnership, and

■   Alison Amsterdam's share of profits and income.

PARTNERSHIP STATEMENT (SHORT) *for the year ended 5 April 2011*

Please read these instructions before completing the Statement

Use these pages to allocate partnership income if the only income for the relevant return period was trading and professional income or taxed interest and alternative finance receipts from banks and building societies. Otherwise you must ask the SA Orderline for the *Partnership Statement (Full)* pages to record details of the allocation of all the partnership income.

Step 1 Fill in boxes 1 to 29 and boxes A and B as appropriate. Get the figures you need from the relevant boxes in the Partnership Tax Return. Complete a separate Statement for each accounting period covered by this Partnership Tax Return and for each trade or profession carried on by the partnership.

Step 2 Then allocate the amounts in boxes 11 to 29 attributable to each partner using the allocation columns on this page and page 7 (see pages PTRG 21 to 25 of the Partnership Tax Return Guide for help). If the partnership has more than three partners, please photocopy page 7.

Step 3 Each partner will need a copy of their allocation of income to fill in their personal tax return.

PARTNERSHIP INFORMATION
If the partnership business includes a trade or profession, enter here the accounting period for which appropriate items in this statement are returned.

Start **1** / /

End **2** / /

Nature of trade **3**

MIXED PARTNERSHIPS

Tick here if this Statement is drawn up using Corporation Tax rules **4**

Tick here if this Statement is drawn up using tax rules for non-residents **5**

Individual partner details

6 Name of partner

Address

Postcode

Date appointed as a partner (if during 2009–10 or 2010–11) **7** / /

Partner's Unique Taxpayer Reference (UTR) **8**

Date ceased to be a partner (if during 2009–10 or 2010–11) **9** / /

Partner's National Insurance number **10**

Partnership's profits, losses, income, tax credits, etc.

Tick this box if the items entered in the box had foreign tax taken off

Partner's share of profits, losses, income, tax credits, etc.

Copy figures in boxes 11 to 29 to boxes in the individual's Partnership (short) pages as shown below

• **for an accounting period ended in 2010–11** ▼					
from box 3.83 Profit from a trade or profession **A**	**11** £	Profit **11** £			Copy this figure to box 7
from box 3.82 Adjustment on change of basis	**11A** £	**11A** £			Copy this figure to box 9
from box 3.84 Loss from a trade or profession **B**	**12** £	Loss **12** £			Copy this figure to box 7
• **for the period 6 April 2010 to 5 April 2011***					
from box 7.9A UK taxed interest and taxed alternative finance receipts	**22** £	**22** £			Copy this figure to box 26
from box 3.97 CIS deductions made by contractors on account of tax	**24** £	**24** £			Copy this figure to box 28
from box 3.98 Other tax taken off trading income	**24A** £	**24A** £			Copy this figure to box 29
from box 7.8A Income Tax taken off	**25** £	**25** £			Copy this figure to box 27
from box 3.117 Partnership charges	**29** £	**29** £			Copy this figure to box 4, 'Other tax reliefs' section on page Ai 2 in your personal tax return

* if you are a 'CT Partnership' see page PTRG 5 of the Partnership Tax Return Guide

HMRC 12/10   PARTNERSHIP TAX RETURN: PAGE 6

Business taxation

Practice assessment 2

This Assessment is based on a sample assessment provided by the AAT and is reproduced here with their kind permission.

Section 1

Task 1.1

For the following, tick if they are revenue or capital based.

✓

	Capital	**Revenue**
Motor car		
Rent		
Repairs		

Task 1.2

Mr Zhang is in business as a sole trader.

The business has the following income statement:

	£	£
Turnover		1,210,210
Cost of sales		808,480
Gross profit		401,730
Wages and salaries	125,778	
Rent, rates and insurance	59,221	
Repairs to plant	8,215	
Advertising and entertaining	19,077	
Accountancy and legal costs	5,710	
Motor expenses	53,018	
Telephone and office costs	14,017	
Depreciation	28,019	
Other expenses	92,460	405,515
Loss		(3,785)

Notes include:

		£
1.	Wages and salaries include:	
	Zhang	30,000
	Zhang's wife, who works in the marketing department	18,000

		£
2.	Advertising and entertaining includes:	
	Gifts to customers:	
	Bottles of wine costing £15 each	2,250
	Diaries carrying the business's logo, costing £10 each	400
	Staff Christmas party for 20 employees	1,485

		£
3.	Motor expenses include:	
	Delivery vans	10,403
	Sales manager's car	6,915
	Zhang's car which is only used for private mileage	5,700

		£
4.	Other expenses include:	
	Cost of staff training	3,550
	Subscription to a golf club for Mr Zhang	220

5.   Capital allowances have already been calculated at £9,878

Complete the computation for Mr Zhang.

Task 1.3

Alan started trading on 1 February 2010. He makes up his accounts to 31 December each year. The profits were calculated at:

	£
Period to 31 December 2010	33,000
Year to 31 December 2011	40,500
Year to 31 December 2012	45,000

(a)   The tax year in which he started trading was (select one):

2008/09; 2009/10; 2010/11; 2011/12

(b)   His taxable profits in his first tax year of trading were (select one):

£2,750; £3,000; £5,500; £6,000

(c)   His taxable profits in his second tax year of trading were (select one):

£33,000; £36,375; £40,500; £45,000

(d)   His taxable profits in his third tax year of trading were (select one):

£33,000; £36,375; £40,500; £45,000

(e)   His overlap profits were   £

(f)   His overlap profits are deducted (select one):

	✓
from his first year profits.	
from the profits in the third year of trading.	
from the profits in the final year of trading.	
from any profits chosen by Alan.	

Task 1.4

(a) A trading loss made by a company can only be offset against trading profits from the same trade when carrying the loss forward.

> **True / False**

(b) A capital loss made by a company can be offset against trading profits in the year the loss is made, but only against capital gains in future years.

> **True / False**

(c) Which one of the following statements is correct? (select one)

	✓
A loss made by a sole trader can only be relieved against trading profits made in the same tax year.	
For a loss made by a sole trader to be relieved in the preceding tax year, it must first have been relieved in the current tax year.	
If a loss made by a sole trader is to be relieved in future years, it must be set against the profits arising from the same trade.	
A loss made by a sole trader can be relieved against total income arising in future years.	

(d) A sole trader can restrict the amount of loss carried back so the personal allowances are not lost.

> **True / False**

Task 1.5

Adam and Barrie have been in partnership for many years, making up their accounts to 31 December each year. Their profit sharing ratio was 2:1 respectively.

On 1 May 2011, Charlie joined the partnership and the profit sharing ratio was changed to 3:2:1 for Adam, Barrie and Charlie.

For the year ended 31 December 2011, the trading profit was £90,000.

Calculate the the division of profit and complete the boxes from the options given below. You are also to enter the relevant period in the left-hand box in each case.

	Total £	Adam £	Barrie £	Charlie £
Period to:	A	B	C	

Options:

A = 90,000; 45,000; 30,000; 22,500

B = 60,000; 30,000; 20,000; 15,000; 45,000; 22,500; 15,000; 11,250

C = 45,000; 30,000; 15,000; 10,000; 7,500; 22,500; 11,250; 5,625

	Total £	Adam £	Barrie £	Charlie £
Period to:	D	E	F	G

Options:

D = 90,000; 45,000; 60,000; 67,500

E = 45,000; 22,500; 30,000; 33,750; 15,000; 20,000

F = 30,000; 15,000; 20,000; 22,500

G = 30,000; 15,000; 7,500; 20,000; 22,500; 10,000; 11,250

Task 1.6

When a company has a period of account that exceeds 12 months, how are the following apportioned? Tick the appropriate boxes.

✓

	Time Apportioned	Separate Computation	Period in which arises
Trading income			
Capital allowances			
Rental income (regular amount)			
Interest income			
Chargeable gains			

Task 1.7

A company has the following non-current asset information for the year ended 31 March 2012:

Balances brought forward as at 1 April 2011:

	£
General pool	265,400
Managing Director's car (BMW – 70% private usage)	18,705
Finance Director's car	13,600
Additions:	
Machinery	32,230
Energy saving plant	13,900
Office furniture	22,405
Managing Director's Car (emissions 180 g/km)	32,100
Disposals:	
Machinery	11,250
Managing Director's car (BMW)	15,400

Calculate the total capital allowances and show the balances to carry forward to the next accounting period.

Section 2

Task 2.1

For each item, tick the appropriate box

✓

	Chargeable asset	**Exempt asset**
Vintage car		
Antique vase		
Racehorse		

Task 2.2

Travelers Ltd sold a valuable picture for £12,000 in June 2011. This was bought for £4,000 in August 2000. The indexation factor from August 2000 to June 2011 was 0.379.

Complete the following computation:

Proceeds £

Cost £

Indexation allowance £

Gain £

Chattel exemption £

Task 2.3

Pressure Ltd bought 5,000 shares in Lucky Ltd for £15,500 in October 2001. A rights issue of 1 for 50 shares was bought in July 2003 for £2 per share. In June 2011, Pressure Ltd sold all the shares for £9 per share.

Indexation factors were: October 2001 to July 2003: 0.114; July 2003 to June 2011: 0.297

What is the gain made on these shares? Use the tables below for your calculations.

	Number of shares	Cost £	Indexed Cost £

Proceeds	
Indexed cost	
Gain	

Task 2.4

(1) Which of the following statements is correct? (select one)

✓

(a)	A capital loss made by an individual can be carried back against capital gains made in the preceding tax year.	
(b)	A capital loss made by an individual can be carried forward to the following tax year without offsetting it against the current year gains.	
(c)	A capital loss made by an individual is offset against gains in the following tax year but only to the extent that it reduces those gains to the amount of the annual exemption.	
(d)	A capital loss made by an individual can only be carried forward for one tax year.	

(2) An individual higher rate tax payer made a capital gain on the sale of his business of £400,000. The rate of tax using entrepreneurial relief is: (select one)

40%;   28%;   10%;   0%

(3) Which of the following statements is correct? (select one)

✓

(a)	Entrepreneurial relief is restricted to £10,000,000 for the lifetime of the taxpayer.	
(b)	Entrepreneurial relief is restricted to £10,000,000 for each capital disposal.	
(c)	Entrepreneurial relief has no restrictions.	
(d)	Entrepreneurial relief is restricted to £400,000 for the lifetime of the taxpayer.	

(4) Anna gifts an asset to George. The asset originally cost Anna £7,000. On the date of the gift, the asset had a market value of £20,000. Anna and George claim gift relief.

Which of the following statements is correct? (select one)   ✓

George's deemed cost is £20,000.	
George's deemed cost is £7,000.	
George's deemed cost is £13,000.	
Anna will pay Capital Gains Tax on the gain of £13,000.	

Task 2.5

(a)   A factory was bought by a sole trader for £400,000 in January 2000. In October 2011, it was sold for £600,000. In the same month another factory was bought for £550,000. The amount of the gain that can be rolled over is:

£ [   ]

Available options: £400,000; £600,000; £550,000; £200,000; £150,000; £50,000

(b)   An asset was sold on 1 November 2009. To obtain rollover relief, the dates during which the proceeds must be reinvested are between:

A [   ]   and   B [   ]

Available options for A: 1 November 2009; 1 November 2010; 1 November 2008; 6 April 2009; 5 April 2010

Available options for B: 1 November 2010; 1 November 2011; 1 November 2012; 1 November 2013; 5 April 2010; 5 April 2011; 5 April 2012

Task 2.6

Indexation allowance is applied to both bonus issues and rights issues of shares when gains are calculated for a company

True / False

Task 2.7

(1)   A taxpayer has self employed income of £70,000 for the tax year 2011/12. The amount chargeable to NIC at 2% would be

£ _____

(2)   A taxpayer has self employed income of £25,000 for 2011/12. The amount of total Class 4 NIC payable would be

£ _____

(3)   Which of the following statements is correct?

✓

(a) Every self employed taxpayer must pay Class 2 NIC, irrespective of the level of profits	
(b) Self employed taxpayers pay either Class 2 or Class 4, but not both	
(c) Class 4 NIC is based on the amount of money taken out of the business by the taxpayer	
(d) In a partnership, each partner is responsible for their own NIC	

Task 2.8

For each of the following, enter the appropriate date:

(1)   First instalment for tax year 2011/12 _____

(2)   Second instalment for tax year 2011/12 _____

(3)   Final instalment for tax year 2011/12 _____

(4)   Payment date for capital gains for 2011/12 _____

Task 2.9

A company has the following information for the year ended 31 March 2012:

TTP is £625,000.

Dividends received, net, are £49,500.

The company has one associated company.

The computation for corporation payable is as follows (enter the amounts and date in the appropriate boxes):

[ ] @ 26%		[ ]
Marginal Relief:		
3/200 ([ ] — [ ]) X [____]		[ ]
Corporation Tax Payable		[ ]
Date of payment		[ ]

Task 2.10

Tick the appropriate box for each of the following statements: ✓

		True	False
(a)	An individual must retain their tax records for 2011/12 until 5 April 2017.		
(b)	If an individual is eight months late in returning their tax return for 2011/12, they will receive a penalty of £200.		
(c)	Penalties for errors made by individuals in their tax return vary from 20% to 100%.		
(d)	If a company fails to keep records for the appropriate period of time, they can only be fined up to £2,000.		
(e)	A company with a period of account ending on 30 April 2011, must keep their records until 30 April 2017.		
(f)	Surcharges can be imposed on late balancing payments.		

Task 2.11

A sole trader has partly completed page 2 of his self-employment tax return, shown on the next page.

Included in the expenses listed in the tax return, the following information is relevant:

(a)   The sole trader has taken drawings of £30,000. This is included in the salaries.

(b)   Advertising and entertaining includes: £

Gifts to customers:

Bottles of wine costing £15 each	2,250
Diaries carrying the business's logo, costing £10 each	400
Staff Christmas party for 20 employees	1,485

(c)   Motor expenses include: £

Delivery vans	10,403
Sales manager's car	6,915
The sole trader's car, (100% private usage)	5,700

Complete boxes 31 to 45

Business expenses

Read pages SEFN 7 to SEFN 9 of the *notes* before completing this section.

Total expenses

If your annual turnover was below £70,000 you may just put your total expenses in box 30

Disallowable expenses

Use this column if the figures in boxes 16 to 29 include disallowable amounts

	Total expenses	Disallowable expenses
16 Cost of goods bought for resale or goods used	£ 8 0 8 4 8 0 · 0 0	**31** £ · 0 0
17 Construction industry - *payments to subcontractors*	£ · 0 0	**32** £ · 0 0
18 Wages, salaries and other staff costs	£ 1 2 5 7 7 8 · 0 0	**33** £ · 0 0
19 Car, van and travel expenses	£ 5 3 0 1 8 · 0 0	**34** £ · 0 0
20 Rent, rates, power and insurance costs	£ 5 9 2 2 1 · 0 0	**35** £ · 0 0
21 Repairs and renewals of property and equipment	£ 8 2 1 5 · 0 0	**36** £ · 0 0
22 Phone, fax, stationery and other office costs	£ 1 4 0 1 7 · 0 0	**37** £ · 0 0
23 Advertising and business entertainment costs	£ 1 9 0 7 7 · 0 0	**38** £ · 0 0
24 Interest on bank and other loans	£ · 0 0	**39** £ · 0 0
25 Bank, credit card and other financial charges	£ · 0 0	**40** £ · 0 0
26 Irrecoverable debts written off	£ · 0 0	**41** £ · 0 0
27 Accountancy, legal and other professional fees	£ 5 7 1 0 · 0 0	**42** £ · 0 0
28 Depreciation and loss/profit on sale of assets	£ 2 8 0 1 9 · 0 0	**43** £ · 0 0
29 Other business expenses	£ 9 2 4 6 0 · 0 0	**44** £ · 0 0
30 Total expenses in boxes 16 to 29	£ 1 2 1 3 9 9 5 · 0 0	**45** Total disallowable expenses in boxes 31 to 44 £ · 0 0

Practice assessment 1
– answers

Section 1

Task 1.1

	Capital	Revenue
Repairs to factory roof		✓
Computer software costing £10,000	✓	
Insurance premiums		✓
Second hand van	✓	

Task 1.2

	£
Net profit per accounts	85,975
Add:	
Notional profit on goods for own use	750
Lesley's NIC and pension	8,125
Gifts of whisky	2,800
Costs of tax appeal	2,500
Private car expenses	1,950
Depreciation	22,680
	124,780
Less:	
Capital allowances	20,680
Adjusted profit	104,100

Task 1.3

(a)   The tax year in which she started trading was 2010/11

(b)   Her taxable profits in her first tax year of trading were £48,000

(c)   Her taxable profits in her second tax year of trading were £96,000

(d)   Her taxable profits in her third tax year of trading were £84,000

(e)   Her overlap profits were £24,000

Task 1.4

(e)   either £31,000 or £17,000 or nothing

Task 1.5

(i)

	Total	Ivor	Jo	Kirsty
	£	£	£	£
1 Jan – 31 July 2011	70,000	35,000	21,000	14,000
1 Aug – 31 Dec 2011	50,000	25,000	25,000	0
Total	120,000	60,000	46,000	14,000

(ii)   The trading assessment for 2011/12 for Kirsty is £14,000

Task 1.6

	CAP 12 months to 31/8/2011	CAP 4 months to 31/12/2011
	£	£
Trading Profits before CAs	600,000	200,000
Capital Allowances	54,000	19,000
Trading Profits	546,000	181,000
Chargeable Gains	50,000	41,000
Rental Income	24,000	8,000
Sub total	620,000	230,000
Gift Aid	0	6,000
TTP	620,000	224,000

Task 1.7

CAP FOR THE 12 MONTHS TO 30/6/2011			
	Main Pool	**Single Asset Pool Exp Car (Ford)**	**Capital Allowances**
	£	£	£
WDV bf	105,000	17,000	
add			
Acquisitions with FYAs:			
Low emission car £25,000			
100% FYA £(25,000)			25,000
	0		
Acquisitions qualifying for AIA:			
Computer £90,000			
AIA claimed £(90,000)			90,000
Excess	0		
less			
Proceeds of Disposals	(5,000)		
	100,000	17,000	
WDA 20%	(20,000)	(3,000)	23,000
WDV cf	80,000	14,000	
Total Capital Allowances			138,000

Section 2

Task 2.1

	Chargeable	**Exempt**
Government Stocks (gilts)		✓
Shares in Limited Companies	✓	
Trading Inventory		✓
Land	✓	

Task 2.2

Proceeds: £7,100

Cost: £4,000

Indexation allowance: £1,516

Gain: £1,584

Chattel restriction on gain: £1,833

No. The chattel restriction will not limit the gain.

Task 2.3

	No. Shares	Cost £	Indexed Cost £
Purchase October 2001	9,000	27,900	27,900
Bonus shares	900	0	0
Indexation to July 2003			3,181
Purchase July 2003	5,000	19,000	19,000
Sub total	14,900	46,900	50,081
Indexation to June 2011			14,874
Total	14,900	46,900	64,955
Disposal	(10,000)	(31,477)	(43,594)
Pool Balance	4,900	15,423	21,361

Proceeds   £45,000

Indexed Cost   £43,594

Gain   £1,406

Task 2.4

(d) and (f) are true; (a), (b), (c) and (e) are false.

Task 2.5

(a)

	£
Sale proceeds	400,000
Cost	180,000
Total gain	220,000
Deferred gain	155,000
Gain chargeable immediately	65,000
Annual exempt amount	10,600
Capital Gains Tax payable	5,440

(b)   The cost of the shop will be deemed to be £180,000 when it is ultimately sold.

Task 2.6

    (a)   The gain or loss on the sale of shares on 12 January 2012 is £1,580 loss.

    (b)   The gain or loss on the sale of shares on 31 March 2012 is £9,500 gain.

Task 2.7

    (b), (d), (e) and (f) are correct

Task 2.8

Payment type	Date
First instalment for 2011/12	31/1/2012
Second instalment for 2011/12	31/7/2012
Final balance for 2011/12	31/1/2013
First instalment for 2012/13	31/1/2013
Second instalment for 2012/13	31/7/2013
CGT for 2011/12	31/1/2013

Task 2.9

	£
Maximum of Band	250,000
Minimum of Band	50,000
Corporation Tax at Main Rate	36,400
Marginal Relief	1,650
Corporation Tax Payable	34,750

Task 2.10

    (a), (c) and (f) are true; (b), (d), (e) and (g) are false.

Task 2.11

    See completed form, opposite.

PARTNERSHIP STATEMENT (SHORT) *for the year ended 5 April 2011*

Please read these instructions before completing the Statement

Use these pages to allocate partnership income if the only income for the relevant return period was trading and professional income or taxed interest and alternative finance receipts from banks and building societies. Otherwise you must ask the SA Orderline for the *Partnership Statement (Full)* pages to record details of the allocation of all the partnership income.

Step 1 Fill in boxes 1 to 29 and boxes A and B as appropriate. Get the figures you need from the relevant boxes in the Partnership Tax Return. Complete a separate Statement for each accounting period covered by this Partnership Tax Return and for each trade or profession carried on by the partnership.

Step 2 Then allocate the amounts in boxes 11 to 29 attributable to each partner using the allocation columns on this page and page 7 (see pages PTRG 21 to 25 of the Partnership Tax Return Guide for help). If the partnership has more than three partners, please photocopy page 7.

Step 3 Each partner will need a copy of their allocation of income to fill in their personal tax return.

PARTNERSHIP INFORMATION

If the partnership business includes a trade or profession, enter here the accounting period for which appropriate items in this statement are returned.

Start	**1**	1 / 4 /1 1
End	**2**	3 1/ 3 /1 2
Nature of trade	**3**	Wholesale Fabric

MIXED PARTNERSHIPS

Tick here if this Statement is drawn up using Corporation Tax rules **4**

Tick here if this Statement is drawn up using tax rules for non-residents **5**

Individual partner details

6 Name of partner   Alison Amsterdam

Address

Postcode

Date appointed as a partner (if during 2009–10 or 2010–11)

7 / /

Partner's Unique Taxpayer Reference (UTR)

8

Date ceased to be a partner (if during 2009–10 or 2010–11)

9 / /

Partner's National Insurance number

10

Partnership's profits, losses, income, tax credits, etc.

Tick this box if the items entered in the box had foreign tax taken off

Partner's share of profits, losses, income, tax credits, etc.

Copy figures in boxes 11 to 29 to boxes in the individual's Partnership (short) pages as shown below

• for an accounting period ended in 2010–11 ▼			
from box 3.83 Profit from a trade or profession **A**	**11** £ 80,000	Profit **11** £ 48,000	*Copy this figure to box 7*
from box 3.82 Adjustment on change of basis	**11A** £	**11A** £	*Copy this figure to box 9*
from box 3.84 Loss from a trade or profession **B**	**12** £	Loss **12** £	*Copy this figure to box 7*
• for the period 6 April 2010 to 5 April 2011*			
from box 7.9A UK taxed interest and taxed alternative finance receipts	**22** £ 2,000	**22** £ 1,200	*Copy this figure to box 26*
from box 3.97 CIS deductions made by contractors on account of tax	**24** £	**24** £	*Copy this figure to box 28*
from box 3.98 Other tax taken off trading income	**24A** £	**24A** £	*Copy this figure to box 29*
from box 7.8A Income Tax taken off	**25** £	**25** £	*Copy this figure to box 27*
from box 3.117 Partnership charges	**29** £	**29** £	*Copy this figure to box 4, 'Other tax reliefs' section on page Ai 2 in your personal tax return*

* if you are a 'CT Partnership' see page PTRG 5 of the Partnership Tax Return Guide

Practice assessment 2
– answers

Section 1

Task 1.1

	Capital	Revenue
Motor car	✓	
Rent		✓
Repairs		✓

Task 1.2

	£	£
Net loss		(3,785)
Add:		
Depreciation	28,019	
Zhang's salary	30,000	
Gifts to customers	2,250	
Subscription to golf club	220	
Motor expenses for Zhang's car	5,700	66,189
		62,404
Less:		
Capital allowances		9,878
Adjusted trading profits		52,526

Task 1.3

(a)   The tax year in which he started trading was 2009/10

(b)   His taxable profits in his first tax year of trading were £6,000

(c)   His taxable profits in his second tax year of trading were £36,375

(d)   His taxable profits in his third tax year of trading were £40,500

(e)   His overlap profits were £9,375

(f)   His overlap profits are deducted from the profits in the final year of trading

Task 1.4

(a)   True

(b)   False

(c)   The following statement is correct:

   If a loss made by a sole trader is to be relieved in future years, it must be set against the profits arising from the same trade.

(d)   False

Task 1.5

	Total £	Adam £	Barrie £	Charlie £
Period to: 30 April 2011	30,000	20,000	10,000	

	Total £	Adam £	Barrie £	Charlie £
Period to: 31 December 2011	60,000	30,000	20,000	10,000

Task 1.6

	Time Apportioned	Separate Computation	Period in which arises
Trading income	✓		
Capital allowances		✓	
Rental income (regular amount)	✓		
Interest income			✓
Chargeable gains			✓

Task 1.7   Capital Allowance Computation

	General Pool	Exp Car BMW	Exp Car FD's	Special Rate Pool	Capital Allowances
	£	£	£	£	£
WDV bf	265,400	18,705	13,600		
add					
Acquisitions without AIA or FYA: Car for Man Director				32,100	
Acquisitions with FYA: Energy saving plant 13,900					
100% FYA (13,900)					13,900
Acquisitions qualifying for AIA:					
Machinery 32,230					
Furniture 22,405					
AIA (54,365)	0				54,635
less Disposals	(11,250)	(15,400)			
	254,150	3,305	13,600	32,100	
20% WDA	(50,830)		(2,720)		53,550
10% WDA				(3,210)	3,210
Bal allowance		(3,305)			3,305
WDV cf	203,320	0	10,880	28,890	
Total Capital Allowances					128,600

Section 2

Task 2.1

	Chargeable asset	Exempt asset
Vintage car		✓
Antique vase	✓	
Racehorse		✓

Task 2.2

Proceeds: £12,000

Cost: £4,000

Indexation allowance: £1,516

Gain: £6,484

Chattel exemption: £10,000

Task 2.3

	No of shares	Cost £	Indexed Cost £
October 2001	5,000	15,500	15,500
Indexation			1,767
Sub total			17,267
Rights Issue	100	200	200
Sub total	5,100	15,700	17,467
Indexation			5,188
Sub total			22,655
Disposal	(5,100)	(15,700)	(22,655)

Proceeds	£45,900
Indexed Cost	£22,655
Gain	£23,245

Task 2.4

(1)   (c) is correct

(2)   10%

(3)   (a) is correct

(4)   George's deemed cost is £7,000

Task 2.5

    (a)   £150,000

    (b)   1 November 2008 and 1 November 2012

Task 2.6

    False

Task 2.7

    (1)   £27,525

    (2)   £1,599.75

    (3)   (d) is correct

Task 2.8

    (1)   First instalment for tax year 2011/12: 31 January 2012

    (2)   Second instalment for tax year 2011/12: 31 July 2012

    (3)   Final instalment for tax year 2011/12: 31 January 2013

    (4)   Payment date for capital gains for 2011/12: 31 January 2013

Task 2.9

625,000 @ 26%	£162,500
Marginal Relief:	
3/200 (750,000 – 680,000) x (625,000/680,000)	£965
Corporation Tax Payable	£161,535

Date of payment: 1/1/2013

Task 2.10

		True	False
(a)	An individual must retain their tax records for 2011/12 until 5 April 2017.		✓
(b)	If an individual is eight months late in returning their tax return for 2011/12, they will receive a penalty of £200.	✓	
(c)	Penalties for errors made by individuals in their tax return vary from 20% to 100%.		✓
(d)	If a company fails to keep records for the appropriate period of time, they can only be fined up to £2,000.		✓
(e)	A company with a period of account ending on 30 April 2011, must keep their records until 30 April 2017.	✓	
(f)	Surcharges can be imposed on late balancing payments.	✓	

Task 2.11

Business expenses

Read pages SEFN 7 to SEFN 9 of the *notes* before completing this section.

Total expenses

If your annual turnover was below £70,000 you may just put your total expenses in box 30

Disallowable expenses

Use this column if the figures in boxes 16 to 29 include disallowable amounts

16 Cost of goods bought for resale or goods used

£ 8 0 8 4 8 0 . 0 0

31

£ . 0 0

17 Construction industry – *payments to subcontractors*

£ . 0 0

32

£ . 0 0

18 Wages, salaries and other staff costs

£ 1 2 5 7 7 8 . 0 0

33

£ 3 0 0 0 0 . 0 0

19 Car, van and travel expenses

£ 5 3 0 1 8 . 0 0

34

£ 5 7 0 0 . 0 0

20 Rent, rates, power and insurance costs

£ 5 9 2 2 1 . 0 0

35

£ . 0 0

21 Repairs and renewals of property and equipment

£ 8 2 1 5 . 0 0

36

£ . 0 0

22 Phone, fax, stationery and other office costs

£ 1 4 0 1 7 . 0 0

37

£ . 0 0

23 Advertising and business entertainment costs

£ 1 9 0 7 7 . 0 0

38

£ 2 2 5 0 . 0 0

24 Interest on bank and other loans

£ . 0 0

39

£ . 0 0

25 Bank, credit card and other financial charges

£ . 0 0

40

£ . 0 0

26 Irrecoverable debts written off

£ . 0 0

41

£ . 0 0

27 Accountancy, legal and other professional fees

£ 5 7 1 0 . 0 0

42

£ . 0 0

28 Depreciation and loss/profit on sale of assets

£ 2 8 0 1 9 . 0 0

43

£ 2 8 0 1 9 . 0 0

29 Other business expenses

£ 9 2 4 6 0 . 0 0

44

£ . 0 0

30 Total expenses in boxes 16 to 29

£ 1 2 1 3 9 9 5 . 0 0

45 Total disallowable expenses in boxes 31 to 44

£ 6 5 9 6 9 . 0 0

for your notes

for your notes

for your notes

for your notes

for your notes

for your notes

for your notes

for your notes

for your notes

for your notes